A Tune A Day

for French Horn.
(F and Bb) and Tenor Horn (Eb)
by C. Paul Herfurth
and Vernon R. Miller.

Book One.

Exclusive Distributors:
Music Sales Limited
14-15 Berners Street, London W1T 3LJ, UK.
Music Sales Pty Limited
20 Resolution Drive, Caringbah, NSW 2229, Australia.

Order No. BM10181
ISBN 0.7119.1569.0

Boston Music Company.

FOREWORD TO TEACHERS

IN compiling this course the objective has intentionally been not to cover too much ground; but rather to concentrate on the acquisition of a thorough musical background and a solid foundation in good horn playing. These two requisites are inseparable.

A brief section is devoted to the simpler rudiments of music which should be thoroughly understood as the need arises.

The learning of new fingerings as introduced should be insisted upon.

Cultivate in the pupil the habit of careful listening.

The familiar hymns and folk-songs have been selected because of their melodic interest as pieces, and because, in addition, in each appears some technical point to be mastered.

The value of learning to " think count " from the very beginning cannot be overestimated. Only in this way can a pupil sense rhythm. Rhythm, one of the most essential elements of music, and usually conspicuous by its absence amateur ensemble playing, is emphasized throughout.

Many teachers do the thinking for their pupils, instead of helping them to think for themselves. Insisting upon the mastery of each point will not dull their interest.

Lessons marked, " Supplementary Material " may be given as a reward for well-prepared work.

Class teaching should be a combination of individual instruction and ensemble playing. At every lesson there should be individual playing so that all the necessary corrections can be made. Never allow pupils' mistakes to go unnoticed, since only by immediate correction will they develop the habit of careful thinking and playing.

A decided advantage of group-teaching is that it provides experience in ensemble playing and gives every pupil the opportunity of listening to the others, of observing their mistakes, and of profiting from the corrections.

For the best results each class should not be made up of more than six for a half-hour lesson, and twelve for an hour lesson. Irrespective of the numbers, the teacher must see to it that there is individual instruction as well as general class direction.

Classes should be regraded whenever necessary so as not to retard the progress of the more gifted students or to discourage the less musically endowed. This procedure also acts as an incentive for greater effort on the part of the pupils.

The lip slurs on page 32 should be used whenever necessary according to the individual student's requirements.

The tests, following each eight lessons, are given as a definite check on the pupil's progress of knowledge and accomplishment. These tests are most important and should not be omitted.

Eventual success in mastering the instrument depends on regular and careful application to its technical demands. Daily practice should not extend beyond the limits of the player's physical endurance—the aim should be the gradual development of lip and breath control alongside assured finger-work.

C. PAUL HERFURTH

VERNON R. MILLER

NOTE: THOSE TEACHERS WHO PREFER G AS THE STARTING NOTE MAY BEGIN ON PAGE 8, LESSON 2B, NOS. 14–15–16–17, THEN GO TO PAGE 7, LESSON 2A, NOS. 7–8–9–10, PAGE 6, LESSON 2, NOS. 1–2–3–4, PAGE 5, LESSON 1A, NOS. 6–7–8–9–10 AND PAGE 4, LESSON 1, NOS. 1–2–3–4, AND PAGE 5 NO. 5.

RUDIMENTS OF MUSIC

Music is represented on paper by a combination of characters and signs, all of which it is necessary to learn in order to play the French Horn intelligently.

Symbols called notes are written upon and between five lines [staff] which is the staff.

The sign [treble clef] placed at the beginning of the staff is called the treble or G clef.

The staff is divided by barlines into bars as follows:

These bars, in turn, are equal in time value, according to the fractional numbers, (Time signature) placed at the beginning of the music.

RUDIMENTS OF MUSIC (cont.)

The time signature indicates the number of notes of equal value in each bar. The upper figure gives the number of beats or counts in a bar, and the lower figure indicates what kind of a note has one beat, such as $\frac{4}{4}$ or **C** equals

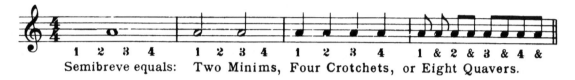

four crotchets or the equivalent minim and two crotchets in each bar; $\frac{2}{4}$ equals 2 crotchets; $\frac{4}{8}$ equals 4 quavers; etc.

There are different kinds of notes, each variety representing a certain time value as follows:

Semibreve equals: Two Minims, Four Crotchets, or Eight Quavers.

The count for the above would be, four to the semibreve: two to each minim: one to each crotchet and one to each group of two quavers.

The notes are named after the first seven letters of the alphabet, i.e., (a, b, c, d, e, f, g) according to the line on or space in which they are placed.

The Treble (G) clef which encircles the second line, establishes the note G on this line, from which

the other lines and spaces are named as follows:

In addition notes are written upon and between short lines above and below the staff. These lines are called leger lines.

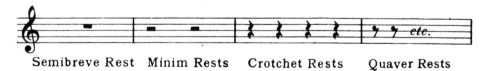

A rest indicates a pause, or silence for the value of the note after which it is named, such as

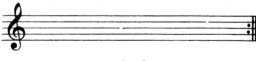

Semibreve Rest   Minim Rests   Crotchet Rests   Quaver Rests

The end of the piece is indicated by a light and heavy line

When a section or part of a piece is to be repeated it will be shown by a double bar with two dots.

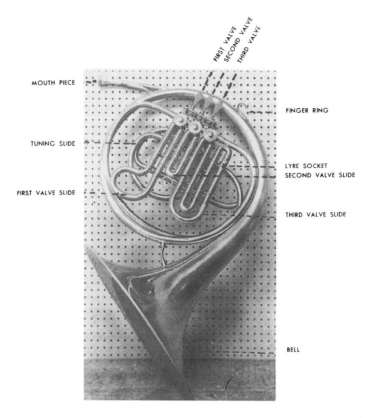

MOUTH PIECE

TUNING SLIDE

FIRST VALVE SLIDE

FIRST VALVE
SECOND VALVE
THIRD VALVE

FINGER RING

LYRE SOCKET
SECOND VALVE SLIDE

THIRD VALVE SLIDE

BELL

CARE OF THE INSTRUMENT

Your horn will not sound its best, nor will your learning to play it be as easy, unless everything pertaining to the instrument is kept in perfect condition.

VALVES: The fingering mechanism for the horn is more varied than any other brass-wind instrument. Have your teacher show you how to disassemble, clean, adjust and reassemble the particular type of mechanism on your horn.

TUNING AND VALVE SLIDES: These slides, as well as the valve caps, should be greased with a little vaseline to keep them free. Try them twice a week.

MOUTHPIECE AND TUBING: Unless you clean the inside of your instrument, a coating of saliva will form which will greatly interfere with its playing qualities. At least once a week run lukewarm soap suds through your instrument. Hold the valves down while pouring water into the bell. Be sure to rinse with clear warm water. Take pride in the way your instrument looks by keeping it bright and clean.

FAILURE ON YOUR PART IN FOLLOWING OUT REGULARLY THE ABOVE INSTRUCTIONS IN REGARD TO THE CARE OF YOUR INSTRUMENT WILL RESULT IN EXPENSIVE REPAIR COSTS.

FOREWORD TO STUDENTS

PHYSICAL PREPARATION

Various ways may be used to help the beginning student produce his first note. The following is one method that has proved successful.

Close the lips and then gradually pull back the corners of the mouth until the lip surfaces are even. (Do not stretch the the lips tightly). Take a breath, and, gently blowing, produce a " buzzing sound ". The lips must vibrate in the very centre while producing the " buzz ". When you are able to " buzz " steadily you are ready to place the mouthpiece to the lips.

It is considered good practice to place the mouthpiece half on the upper lip and half on the lower lip in the centre of the mouth. (See pictures.) An abnormal mouth formation or tooth structure may necessitate modifications of the above, but in general, it is good to strive to form the embouchure as closely as possible like the above.

The tip of the tongue is placed behind the upper teeth, and when ready to produce a note, jerk the tongue downwards by using the syllable " TU ". The tongue must be moved very quickly. Breath should be taken through the corners of the mouth. DO NOT PUFF OUR YOUR CHEEKS. Practise in front of a mirror.

METHOD OF HOLDING THE FRENCH HORN

The French Horn is supported in three ways: (1) by the right hand which is placed inside the bell (see Fig. 1); (2) the bell which rests on the inner aspect of the thigh of the right leg (see Fig. 1); (3) by the left hand. Place the palm of the left hand so it rests on the large tubing opposite the valves, put the little finger in the finger ring and the thumb under the small tubing which leads to the mouthpiece. When the little finger and thumb are in place, arch the other fingers slightly and let them rest in position on the levers (see Fig. 2). The first finger for the first valve (nearest the mouthpiece) marked (1); the second finger for the second valve marked (2); the third finger for the third valve marked (3).

Fig. 1

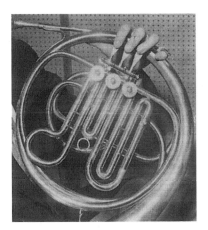

Fig. 2

Correct Sitting Position

Correct Standing Position

EMBOUCHURE

There are two accepted types of French Horn embouchure; the " set in " type and the " set on " type. Those illustrated are the " set on " type. Your teacher will use that which will be most suitable for you and/or the type with which he is more successful.

Pictures posed by Robert Handy; East Orange, N. J.

TECHNICAL

The most important technical points for wind instrument players are as follows:

(1) Developing and strengthening the lip muscles.
(Process) Playing of long sustained notes.

(2) Developing clarity and precision in attack.
(Process) Proper use of the tongue.

(3) Developing a fine quality of tone.
(Process) A combination of No. 1 and careful listening.

(4) Developing fluency in fingering.
(Process) Playing of scales and arpeggios in various keys.

(5) Developing a mastery of the entire range of the instrument.
(Process) A combination of all of the above.

[v]

Table of
Harmonics for French Horn

Prepared by W. J. Duthoit

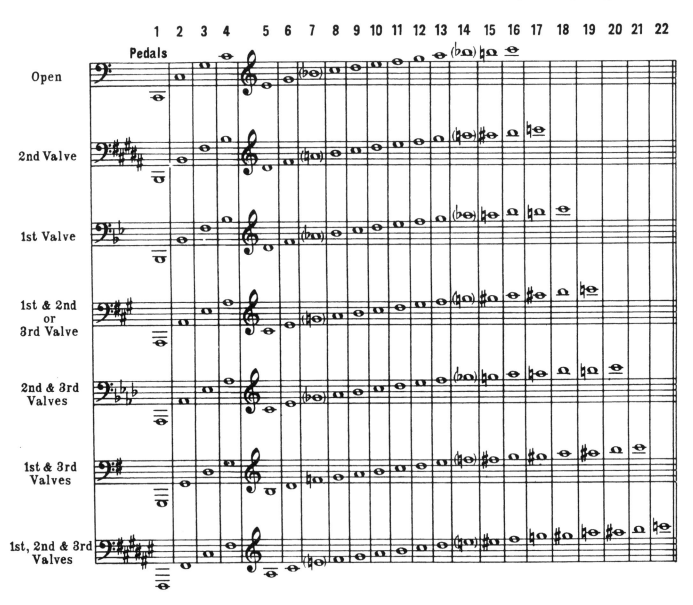

N.B. 7th & 14th Harmonics are flat

11th Harmonics are sharp

Reference Fingering Chart
for
F Horn

Correct fingerings for all natural notes within the normal range of the F horn. The notes within the bracket indicate the range used in this book.

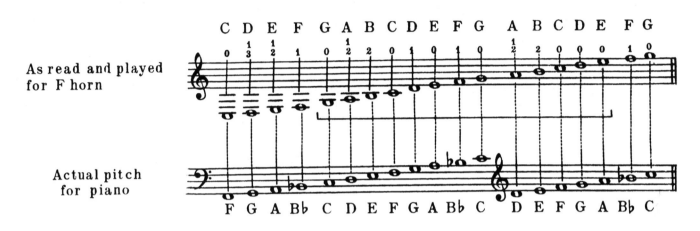

As read and played for F horn

Actual pitch for piano

ENHARMONIC NOTES: Notes that sound the same, and are fingered the same, but are written differently. Those most frequently used are the following:

Reference Fingering Chart
for
B♭ Horn

Correct fingerings for all natural notes within the normal range of the B♭ horn. The notes within the bracket indicate the range used in this book.

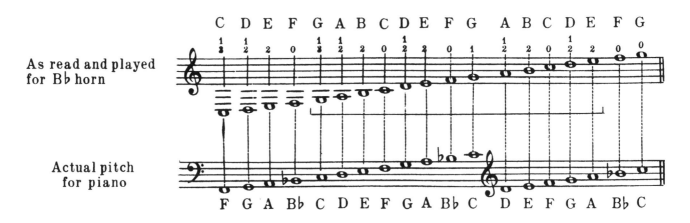

ENHARMONIC NOTES: Notes that sound the same, and are fingered the same, but are written differently. Those most frequently used are the following:

Reference Fingering Chart
for
E♭ Horn (Tenor)

Correct fingerings for all natural notes within the normal range of the E♭ horn. The notes within the bracket indicate the range used in this book.

As read and played for E♭ horn

Actual pitch for piano

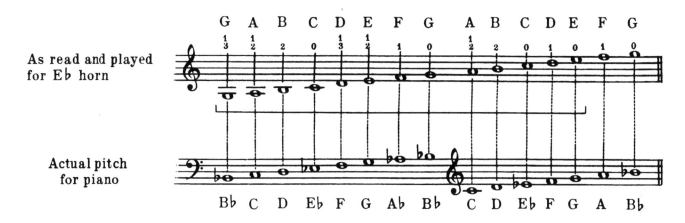

ENHARMONIC NOTES: Notes that sound the same, and are fingered the same, but are written differently. Those most frequently used are the following:

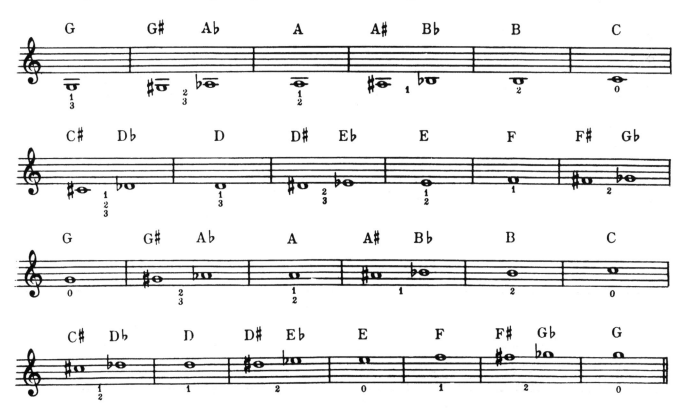

A TUNE A DAY
LESSON 1

OBJECTIVES: 1. To learn the correct habits of
    (a) Holding the French Horn or E flat Horn.
    (b) Position of mouthpiece "set on" or "set in".
    2. To correlate the valves of the horn
      with the notes on the staff. C - D
    3. To know the value of minims crotchets and their equivalent rests.
    4. To know the meaning of the repeat sign.
    5. Answer all questions and do homework.

MINIMS (2 Count notes)  and MINIM (2 Count) RESTS

Introducing 1st leger line below the staff C.

Played open, no valves.
Play C as long as possible. Do this many times. Think of a straight line and try to make the note(pitch) stay on the line.

This note is C and is played open. No valves.

Think Count: 1 2 3 4   REPEAT

This note is ___ and is played ___ ?

Think Count: 1 2 3 4

CROTCHETS (1 Count notes) and CROTCHET (1 Count) RESTS

CROTCHET REST

Think Count: 1 2 3 4

These are _____ and receive ____ count?

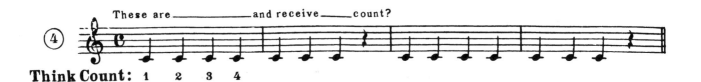

Think Count: 1 2 3 4

LESSON 1a

Minims and Crotchets

Numbers 11 and 12 are to be used only if C has been used as the starting note.

Little C and D March

Think Count: 1 2 3 4

Home work: Write a line of crotchets (♩) and minims (♩) using C and D. Mark the letter name above and the fingering (valves used) below each note.

LESSON 2

OBJECTIVES: 1. Continuation of the objectives of lesson 1.
2. To learn the names and fingerings of the new notes E-F-G.
3. To learn the meaning of the breath mark (ʾ).
4. Answer all questions.

Introducing 1st line E

F Horn
0
2 (1)(2)
Bb Horn
Eb Horn

Play E as long as possible. Do this many times. Think of a straight line and try to make the note (pitch) stay on the line.

Preparation

C D E

This note is E and is played with the
——VALVES ON THE F HORN
——VALVE ON THE Bb HORN
——VALVES ON THE Eb HORN

①

Think Count: 1 2 3 4 ,
These are ___minim___ and receive ___2___ counts?

②

Think Count: 1 2 3 4

③

Think Count: 1 2 3 4
These are ___crochet___ and ___l___ rests and each receives ___l___ count?

④

Numbers 5 and 6 are to be used only if C has been used as the starting note.

This note is ___?

⑤

Think Count: 1 2 3 4

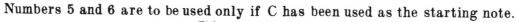

Melody

⑥

Think Count: 1 2 3 4

Introducing 1st space F

F Horn 1

Bb Horn 0 (1) **Eb Horn**

Play F as long as possible. Do this many times. Think of a straight line and try to make the note (pitch) stay on the line.

Preparation C D E F

This note is **F** and is played with the
____VALVE ON THE F HORN
____VALVES ON THE Bb HORN
____VALVE ON THE Eb HORN

⑦

Think Count: 1 2 3 4

These are _____ and receive _____ counts?

⑧

Think Count: 1 2 3 4

⑨

Think Count: 1 2 3 4

These are _____ and _____ rests and each receives _____ count?

⑩

Numbers 11, 12 and 13 are to be used only if C has been used as the starting note.

This note is ___?

⑪

Think Count: 1 2 3 4

Melody

⑫

Think Count: 1 2 3 4

Melody

⑬

Think Count: 1 2 3 4

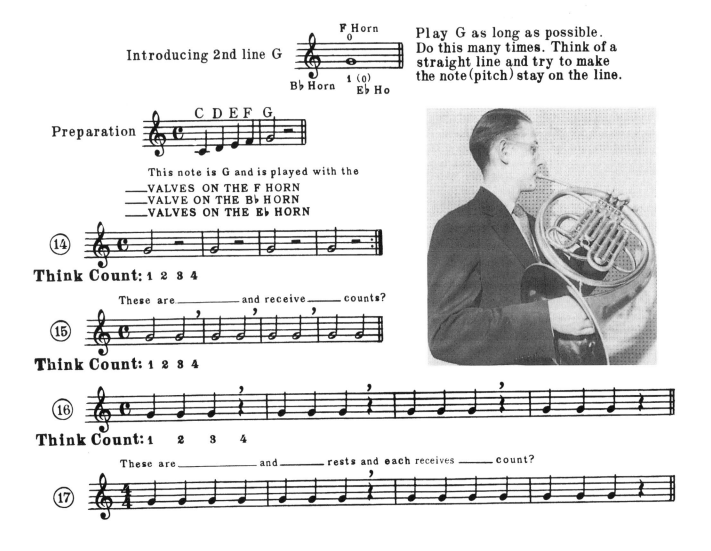

Introducing 2nd line G

Play G as long as possible. Do this many times. Think of a straight line and try to make the note (pitch) stay on the line.

Preparation   C D E F G

This note is G and is played with the

____ VALVES ON THE F HORN
____ VALVE ON THE B♭ HORN
____ VALVES ON THE E♭ HORN

(14)

Think Count: 1 2 3 4

These are _____ and receive _____ counts?

(15)

Think Count: 1 2 3 4

(16)

Think Count: 1   2   3   4

These are _____ and _____ rests and each receives _____ count?

(17)

Numbers 18, 19 and 20 are to be used only if C has been used as the starting note.

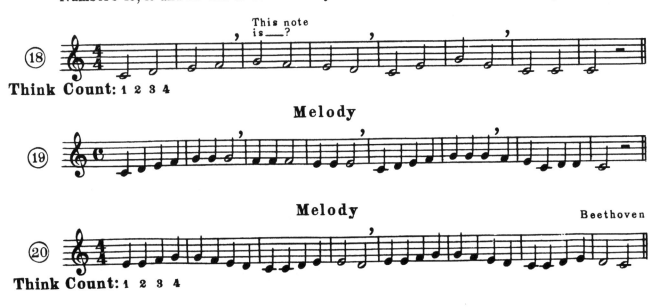

This note is ___?

(18)

Think Count: 1 2 3 4

Melody

(19)

Melody   Beethoven

(20)

Think Count: 1 2 3 4

LESSON 3

OBJECTIVES: 1. To learn the meaning of the TIE.
2. Application of acquired knowledge in playing familiar melodies.
3. Home work.

Tied Notes

When two notes on the same line or space of the staff are joined by a curved line (⌒), they are to be played as one note, adding the value of the two notes together.

Think Count: 1 2 3 4

Think Count: 1 2 3 4

Mary had A Little Lamb

Think Count: 1 2 3 4

Melody

Think Count: 1 2 3 4

Jingle Bells

Think Count: 1 2 3 4

Lightly Row

Think Count: 1 2 3 4

Home work:

Home work: Mark the fingering above, and the letter names below all notes in exercises 3, 4, 5 and 6. On the staff above write a line of notes you have studied so far. Divide into bars using minims and crotchets.

LESSON 4

OBJECTIVES: 1. To learn the value of a semibreve
2. Comparison of different note values.
3. Playing easy duets (both parts).
4. Rhythm practice.
5. Questions and home work.

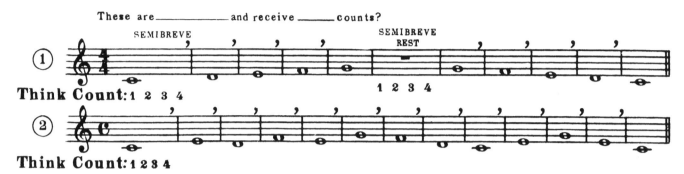

Different Note Values

It is not necessary to play exercise 3 in the order written. Start at the different letters so you are able to hear and sound any note.

Home work: Before playing No. 6 write in the counts. Be sure to put the number of the count directly below the note or rest to which it belongs.

LESSON 5

OBJECTIVES: 1. To learn the meaning of the sharp sign(♯).
2. To learn the name and fingering for first space F♯.
3. To learn the meaning of the natural sign(♮).

A SHARP SIGN(♯) RAISES THE NOTE TO WHICH IT APPLIES BY A SEMITONE
A NATURAL SIGN(♮) TAKES AWAY THE EFFECT OF A SHARP OR FLAT.

Notice the F♯ at the beginning of pieces 4 and 5B. This means that every F throughout the piece will be played sharp.

Folk Song

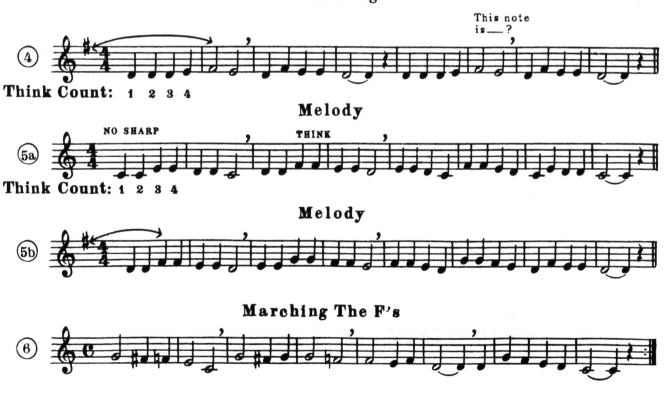

LESSON 6

OBJECTIVES: 1. To learn the name and fingering for
second space (A).
2. Interval and rhythm practice.
3. Application of acquired knowledge in playing
familiar melodies.

Introducing 2nd space A

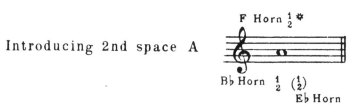

Think Count: 1 2 3 4

Think Count: 1 2 3 4

Oats and Beans

Think Count: 1 2 3 4

Theme From Good King Wenceslas

Long, Long Ago

Folk Song

* Some horn players and teachers prefer to play A with the 3rd finger on the F Horn. On some
horns the 3rd finger F is in better tune. It may also be used to facilitate fingering in rapid
passages.

LESSON 7

OBJECTIVES: 1. To learn to listen to a harmony part.
2. To learn to release and attack notes together.

Upidee

Upidee

We Two

V. R. M.

Au clair de la lune

LESSON 8

OBJECTIVES: 1. To learn to connect notes (slur).
               2. To learn the meaning of the accidental.

Melody

Rousseau

Abide With Me

Monk

The F♯ in the seventh bar is called an accidental because there are no sharps at the beginning of the piece.

Lightly Row

Supplementary Material for Lessons 1-8

Twinkle, Twinkle Little Star

The Boat Song

C. P. H.

Melody

French Folk Song

TEST QUESTIONS ON LESSONS 1-8

Questions from this, and following test-sheets, will be given as a check on your home-study of preceding lessons.

REMEMBER: The more you know and understand about the signs and symbols used in music-writing, the easier it will be for you to learn how to play well.

	Points	Your score

(1) This ▦ is called?_____ 4 _____

(2) This symbol 𝄞 is called?_____ 4 _____

(3) The staff is divided by bar-lines into?_____ 4 _____

(4) Fractions at the beginning of music are called _____ signatures? 4 _____

(5) This 𝄞 4/4 o is a _____ and has _____ counts? 4 _____

(6) These 𝄞 4/4 are_____ and have _____ counts each? 4 _____

(7) These 𝄞 4/4 are_____ and have_____ count each? 4 _____

(8) Lines and spaces are named after the first_____ letters of the alphabet? 4 _____

(9) This 𝄞 4/4 is a _____ rest? 4 _____

(10) These 𝄞 4/4 are_____ rests? 4 _____

(11) These 𝄞 4/4 are_____ rests? 4 _____

(12) This 𝄞 C or 4/4 means _____ to each bar? 4 _____

(13) This ♯ is a?_____ How does it affect a note?_____ 2 _____

(14) This ♮ is a?_____ How does it affect a note?_____ 2 _____

(15) A curved line joining two notes of the same letter name is called _____? 2 _____

(16) A curved line joining two or more notes of different letter names is called _____ ? 3 _____

(17) Write the notes thus far studied. 𝄞 7 _____

(18) Write the letter name above and the fingering below the following notes: 8 _____

(19) Sight reading test 8

𝄞 C

TEACHER: Write line of notes thus far studied, using semibreves, minims and crotchets as a sight reading test.

(20) Inspection of instrument. 20 _____
This inspection should be followed up at each test period. 100

LESSON 9

OBJECTIVES: 1. To learn the name and fingering for third line B flat.
2. To learn the meaning of a flat (♭).
3. To learn the meaning and use of key signatures.

Introducing 3rd line B♭

A FLAT SIGN(♭) LOWERS THE
NOTE TO WHICH IT APPLIES
BY A SEMITONE.

KEY SIGNATURES: The sharps or flats found after the clef at the beginning of each line is called the key signature. These sharps or flats affect all the notes of the same name throughout the piece, except when changed by a new key signature or temporarily by an accidental.

THE FIRST THING YOU SHOULD LOOK FOR IS THE KEY SIGNATURE, THE SECOND THING, THE TIME SIGNATURE.

The flat sign(♭) placed on the third line of the staff, just after the clef sign, means to flatten every B, except where cancelled by a natural sign(♮).

Home work: Before playing No. 7 write in the counts. Be sure to put the number of the count directly below the note or rest to which it belongs.

LESSON 10

OBJECTIVES: 1. To learn the name and fingering for third line B (natural).
2. Continued emphasis on rhythm and fingering.
3. Practice in recognizing key signatures.
4. Playing of duet with independent parts.

Introducing 3rd line B♮

Think Count: 1 2 3 4

Think Count: 1 2 3 4

Melody

Key of ___ sharp is ___?

This note is ___?

Think Count: 1 2 3 4

Folk Song

Think Count: 1 2 3 4

Harvest Time

C. P. H.

Key of C (No flats or sharps)

Think Count: 1 2 3 4

Rhythm Drill

Home work:
Key of ___ flat is ___?

Home work: Before playing No. 7 write in the counts. Be sure to put the number of the count directly below the note or rest to which it belongs.

Hymn

This time signature means ___ counts in each bar and a _____ receives ___ count.

Think Count: 1 2 3 4

Twinkle, Twinkle Little Star

This time signature means ___ counts in each bar and a _____ receives ___ count.

Duet

V. R. M.

Pupil

Think Count: 1 2 3 4

Pupil

UP BEAT: Many pieces begin with an incomplete bar, usually starting with the last beat or fraction thereof. This is called the up-beat. The ending always completes the bar of the up-beat.

Hymn

Haydn

UP BEAT
Key of___?

The Boat Song

C. P. H.

Key of___ sharp is ___?

LESSON 11

OBJECTIVES: 1. To learn the name and fingering for third
space C.
2. To know the formation of the natural scale,
(Placement of whole- and semitones).
3. Playing the C scale from memory.
4. Continued key practice.

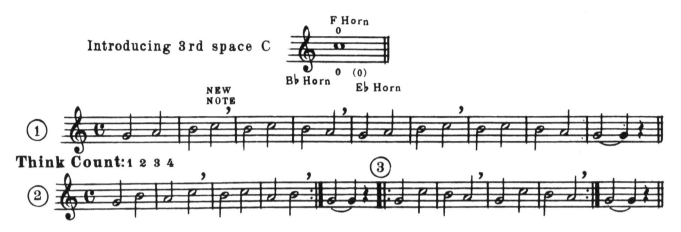

The Scale

A scale is a succession of notes from a given note (key note) to its octave, 8 notes higher. The form on which all major scales are modelled is as follows:

The Natural, or C Major Scale

The ascending progression is: two whole tones, one semitone, three whole tones, one semitone, The semitones come between the numbers 3-4 and 7-8.

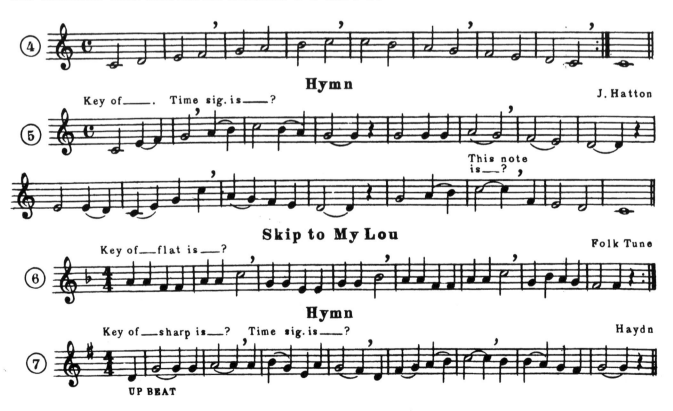

Hymn
J. Hatton

Skip to My Lou
Folk Tune

Hymn
Haydn

LESSON 12

OBJECTIVES: 1. To learn to count and play quavers in
$\frac{4}{4}$ and $\frac{2}{4}$ time.
2. The playing of quavers in familiar and
unfamiliar melodies.

Quavers

A quaver is equal to $\frac{1}{2}$ of a crotchet, and receives $\frac{1}{2}$ of a count in $\frac{4}{4}$ or $\frac{2}{4}$ time. Two quavers equal one crotchet, or one count, four quavers equal one minim (2 counts) and eight quavers equal one semibreve (4 counts).

BE SURE TO LEARN THE RHYTHM DRILLS THOROUGHLY (learn to feel the division of the beats) BEFORE PLAYING THE MELODIES. THIS IS IMPORTANT.

There's Music In The Air

Root

Think Count: 4

Song Of The Volga Boatmen

Key of ___ sharp is ___?

Think Count: 1 & 2 3 4

Polly Wolly Doodle
Duet

Key of ___ flat is ___?

Pupil

Pupil

Peasants' March

Schubert

Home work: Write in the counts before playing

Think Count: 1 & 2 & 1 2 &

Theme From Symphony No.1

Brahms

Home work:

Home work· Write a line of notes thus far studied, using minims, crotchets and quavers in 2 time.

4

LESSON 13

OBJECTIVES: 1. Learning new rhythm—$\frac{3}{4}$ time—with emphasis.
on rhythm drills. (A-B-C etc.).
2. Use of dotted crotchets and quavers.(Ex.F)
3. Application of acquired knowledge.

The Dotted Minim and the Dotted Crotchet

A dot is equal to one half the value of the note it follows. A dotted minim equals 3 beats, a dotted crotchet equals $1\frac{1}{2}$ beats

Rhythm Drills

DRILL: Count aloud each variation, A-B-C etc. while clapping the hands once for each note until the rhythms are felt and memorized, then try to play them using any single note. When this can be done freely, play the exercises as written. REMEMBER—Rhythm must be felt before it can be played.

Combination of Rhythms in $\frac{3}{4}$ time

Home work: Write in the counts before playing.

LESSON 14

OBJECTIVES:
1. Application of $\frac{3}{4}$ and $\frac{2}{4}$ rhythms in familiar melodies of different keys.
2. Continued use of rhythms learned in Lesson 13.
3. Knowledge of the fermata (pause).
4. Knowledge of terms used for tempo (speed).

We Three Kings of Orient Are

Moderate speed(Moderato)

Key of __flat is __? Time sig. is __?

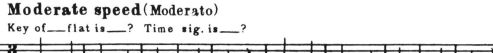

Think Count: 1 2 3

Good King Wenceslas

Key of __sharp is __? Time sig. is __?

Think Count: 1 & 2 &

O Come, All Ye Faithful

Moderato

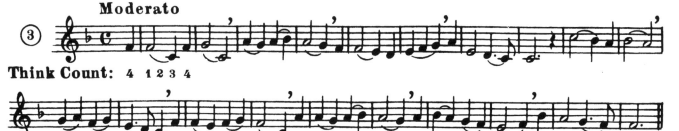

Think Count: 4 1 2 3 4

The First Noel

With motion(Con moto)

Key of __? Time sig. is __?

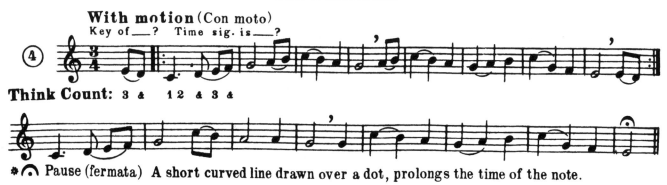

Think Count: 3 & 1 2 & 3 &

✻ 𝄐 Pause (fermata) A short curved line drawn over a dot, prolongs the time of the note.

LESSON 15

OBJECTIVES: 1. To learn the name and fingering for low B,
second space below the staff.
2. Continued use of the rhythms learned in Lesson 13
with special emphasis on the dotted crotchet followed by
a quaver.

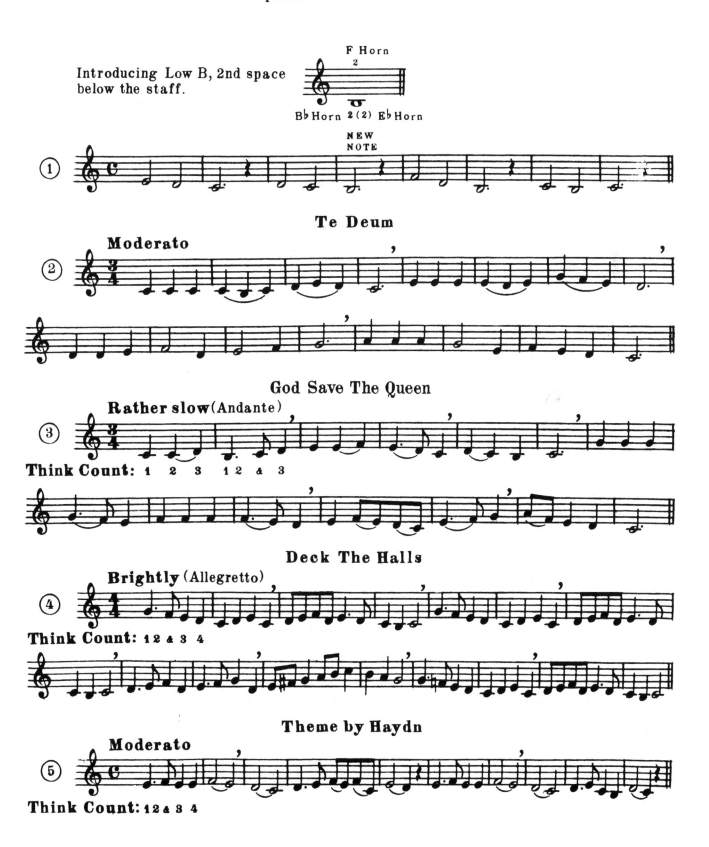

LESSON 16

OBJECTIVES: 1. Continued emphasis on the dotted crotchet followed by a quaver
2. Practise using the after beat in $\frac{3}{4}$ rhythm. (A duet is used to emphasize this objective).
3. Practise using the after beat in Common time or $\frac{4}{4}$ time. (A duet is used to emphasize this objective).

College Song

Moderato

Key of ___ sharp is ___ ?

Think Count: 1 2 & 1 2 &

German Waltz
Duet

Waltz tempo (Tempo di valse)

Pupil

Think Count: 1 2 3

Pupil

1 2 3
AFTER BEATS

Anvil Chorus
Duet

Brightly (Allegretto)

Verdi

Pupil

Think Count: 1 2 3 4 &

Pupil

1 2 3 4
AFTER BEATS

Supplementary Material for Lessons 9-16

Melody

Beethoven

Andante

①

Hymn

F. Kücken

NOTE KEY SIGNATURE
Moderato

②

Listen carefully to the intervals (distance between the notes).

Massa's In The Cold, Cold Ground

Stephen Foster

Andante

③

My Bonnie

College Song

Tempo di Valse

④

TEST QUESTIONS ON LESSONS 9-16

		Points	Your score
(1)	This sign :‖: means?_____	5	_____
(2)	This (♭) is a?_____ How does a (♭) affect a note?_____	7	_____
(3)	The key of one flat is?_____	3	_____
(4)	The key of one sharp is?_____	3	_____
(5)	What is a scale?_____	3	_____
(6)	Write the C major scale	10	_____

		Points	Your score
(7)	Write the key signatures of one flat and one sharp	4	_____

		Points	Your score
(8)	What is an accidental?_____	3	_____
(9)	These are_____?	3	_____
(10)	Each of the above notes receives_____count?	3	_____
(11)	This is a_____?	3	_____
(12)	The above note has_____counts?	3	_____
(13)	This is a_____?	3	_____
(14)	The above note has_____counts?	4	_____
(15)	Divide the following into bars	7	_____

		Points	Your score
(16)	This sign ⌢ means?_____	3	_____
(17)	What is meant by the up beat?_____	3	_____
(18)	On the staff below, write four bars of after beats in $\frac{3}{4}$ time.	5	_____

		Points	Your score
(19)	On the staff below, write four bars of after beats in Common or $\frac{4}{4}$ time.	5	_____

		Points	Your score
(20)	Sight reading.	20	_____
		100	

TEACHER· Write line of notes thus far studied, using semibreves, minims, crotchets, dotted-crotchets and quavers.

LESSON 17

OBJECTIVES: 1. To learn the name and fingering for low B flat,
                  second space below the staff.
            2. To learn the name and fingering for first line E flat.
            3. To memorize the scale of B flat major.
            4. Playing of duet in key of B flat.

LESSON 18

OBJECTIVES : 1. To learn the name and fingering for low A, second leger line below the staff.
2. Playing of duet using quaver after beats in $\frac{2}{4}$ time.
3. Playing of duet using crotchet after beats in $\frac{3}{4}$ time.

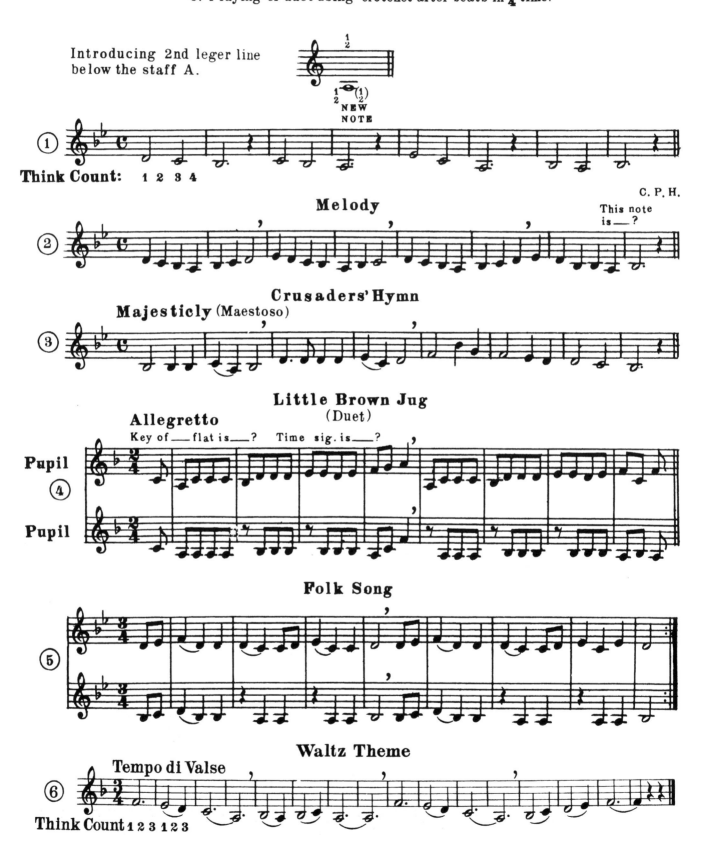

Introducing 2nd leger line below the staff A.

Think Count: 1 2 3 4

Melody

C. P. H.

This note is —?

Crusaders' Hymn

Majesticly (Maestoso)

Little Brown Jug
(Duet)

Allegretto

Key of — flat is —?   Time sig. is —?

Pupil

Pupil

Folk Song

Waltz Theme

Tempo di Valse

Think Count 1 2 3 1 2 3

LESSON 19

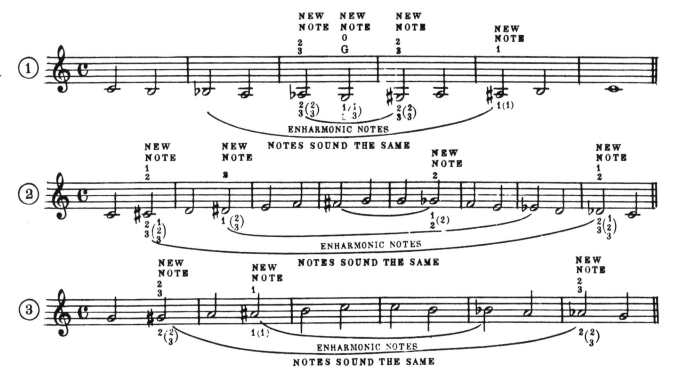

Chromatic Scales

The word "chromatic" means moving by semitones. A chromatic scale is one that ascends or descends by semitones.

If you can't spell a word you can't write it. If you can't spell (recite) a scale you can't play it. Learn to recite all scales before playing.

Scale of G (F♯)

Scale of A (F♯, C♯, G♯)

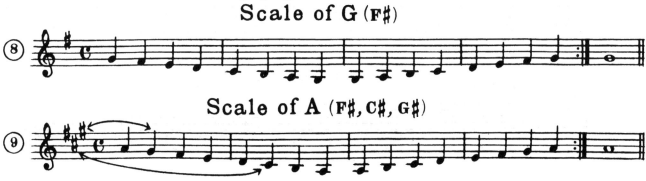

Lip Slurs

OBJECTIVE: Application of proper use of lip muscles and breath
support.

The material in this lesson is to be used as the need arises. The following are suggestions. The
teacher should suggest various patterns of lip slurs to fit the needs of the individual student.

LESSON 20

OBJECTIVES: 1. To learn the name and fingering of fourth line D.
2. Further practice using dotted crotchets followed by quavers.
3. Playing of duet in which melody line changes from one part to another.

Introducing 4th line D

Auld Lang Syne

All Through The Night
(Duet)

Augustin

LESSON 21

OBJECTIVES: 1. To learn the key of D major (F♯ and C♯).
2. To learn the key of A major (F♯, C♯ and G♯).

D Major Scale (F♯, C♯)

Theme from The Second Symphony

Haydn

Key of ___ sharps are ___?

Think Count: 1 2 3 4

Evening Song

Schumann

A Major Scale (F♯, C♯, G♯)

Duet

Hohmann

Key of ___ sharps are ___?

This note is ___?

Think Count: 1 2 3

Supplementary Material for Lessons 17-21

Duet

Weber

Oh! Susanna

Stephen Foster

Now The Day Is Over

Barnby

My Old Kentucky Home

Stephen Foster

LESSON 22

OBJECTIVES: 1. To learn a new rhythm.
2. Understanding Alla breve(cut time) ($\frac{2}{2}$ time).

Comparison of ₵ with $\frac{2}{4}$ time

Rhythm Drill

Drill: Count aloud each pattern while clapping the hands once for each note.
REMEMBER-- Unless you feel a rhythm you cannot play it.
Play the C scale, using these patterns until the rhythms are memorized.

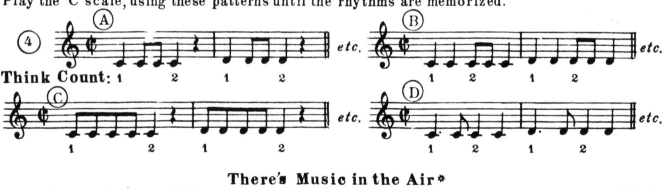

There's Music in the Air*

Compare the bars of this song with ①,②,③,④ above.

G. Root

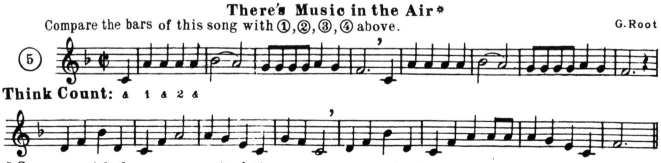

Think Count: & 1 & 2 &

*Compare with the same song in $\frac{4}{4}$ time, page 22, exercise 7.

LESSON 23

OBJECTIVES: Further practice using alla breve

Caisson Song

Maj. E.L. Gruber

March Tempo (Tempo di marcia)

Theme by Haydn

Marines' Hymn

Official Song of the
U.S. Marine Corps

Tempo di Marcia

LESSON 24

OBJECTIVES: 1. Continuation of Alla breve (cut time).
2. The playing of a full length march.
3. Application of acquired knowledge.
4. Knowledge of the meaning of this sign (⅟).
5. Knowledge of signs indicating volume of tone (dynamics).

Advancement March*

C. P. H.

* All marches generally consist of an introduction, 1st and 2nd strain, each repeated, followed by a Trio. The key of the Trio is always a fifth lower than that of the first part.
**This sign ⅟ means to repeat the preceding bar.

TEST QUESTIONS ON LESSONS 17-24

		Points	Your score
(1)	Write the B flat Scale.	10	————

(2) On the scale above, write the name of the note above and the finger- 5 ————
ing below?

(3) The name of this note [music notation] is? _____ 2 ————

(4) The name of this note [music notation] is? _____ 2 ————

(5) The note in No. 3 is played with the _____ valves? 2 ————

(6) The note in No. 4 is played with the _____ valves? 2 ————

(7) What is meant by enharmonic notes? 5 ————

(8) Write the enharmonic equivalents of the following notes. 5 ————

[music notation]

(9) What is meant by chromatics? _____ 5 ————

(10) Write the scale of G major. 10 ————

(11) Write the scale of D major. 10 ————

(12) Write the scale of A major. 10 ————

(13) This sign ¢ means. _____ 2 ————

(14) A minim receives _____ count in alla breve time. 2 ————

(15) Divide the following into bars? 5 ————

[music notation]

(16) This sign ╱ means. _____ 3 ————

(17) Sight reading. 20 ════

100

TEACHER: Write line of notes in alla breve.

LESSON 25

OBJECTIVES: 1. To learn another new rhythm.
2. Knowledge and use of $\frac{6}{8}$ rhythm.
3. To learn to count slow and fast $\frac{6}{8}$ rhythm.
4. Application of new rhythm in familiar melodies.

Think Count: Slow 1 2 3 4 5 6 Fast 1 ___ 2 ___

Think Count: Slow 1 2 3 4 5 6 Fast 1 & uh 2 & uh

Think Count: Slow 1 2 3 4 5 6 Fast 1 & uh 2 & uh

Think Count: Slow 1 2 3 4 5 6 Fast 1 ___ 2 ___

Think Count: Slow 1 2 3 4 5 6 Fast 1 ___ 2 ___

Row, Row, Row Your Boat

Key of___? Time sig. is___?

Think Count: 1 2 1 & 2

Oats and Beans

Key of___flat is___? Time sig. is___?

Think Count: 1 2

Mulberry Bush

Key of___sharp is___? Time sig. is___?

Think Count: 1— 2—

Home work:

Home work: Write line of notes, using different rhythm patterns in $\frac{6}{8}$ time.

Sweet and Low

Barnby

Andante

Think Count: 1 2 3 4 5 6

p (soft) — *gradually louder* — *gradually softer*

mf — *p* — *mf* — *mp (medium soft)* — *p*

Theme from Overture to "Semiramide"

G. A. Rossini

Andante

Think Count: 1 2 3 4 5 6

Drink to Me Only With Thine Eyes

Old English Air

Andante

Key of ____ sharps are ____ ?

Think Count: 1 2 3 4 5 6

mp (medium soft)

mf

gradually softer

mp

* *rit. (slower) and softer*

* rit.- abbreviation of ritenuto - gradually slower in speed.

LESSON 26

OBJECTIVE: Continued practice in fast $\frac{6}{8}$

Barcarolle

Offenbach

Moderato in 2

Skipping Along
(Duet)

C.P.H.

With spirit (Allegro)

Trio of Progress March

C.P.H.

Tempo di Marcia

LESSON 27

OBJECTIVE: Playing of duet in fast $\frac{6}{8}$ with
melody line and characteristic horn
march part.

> = accent

Trio of "Our Director"
March
Duet

F. E. Bigelow

LESSON 28

OBJECTIVES: Learning the use of semiquavers.
         (a) Equivalents
         (b) Counting semiquavers.

Semiquavers

A semiquaver   is equal to half the value of a quaver

Two semiquavers equal one quaver   and four semiquavers equal one crotchet

Abbreviations for semiquavers

Comparative table showing number of semiquavers to other notes studied thus far.

Mac Donald's Farm

Key of ___ sharp is ___?

Home work:

Home work: Write a line of notes, using different groupings of semiquavers in $\frac{2}{4}$ time.

LESSON 29

OBJECTIVES: 1. Dotted quavers and semiquavers legato.
2. Correct division of each beat.
3. Application of new rhythm.

Dotted Quavers and Semiquavers
Legato (Connected)

This is one of the more difficult rhythms to learn. The dotted quaver is equal to three semiquavers.

Always feel a division of four on each beat when playing this rhythm, three on the dotted quaver and one on the semiquaver

BE SURE TO PLAY THE DOTTED QUAVER LONG ENOUGH AND THE SEMIQUAVER SHORT ENOUGH.

Largo
(New World Symphony)
Duet

Dvořák

Home work: Write a line of notes, using dotted quavers and semiquavers.
* cresc.—gradually louder.

LESSON 30

OBJECTIVES: 1. To learn dotted quavers and semiquavers, staccato.
2. Application of this difficult rhythm in familiar
melodies using $\frac{2}{4}$ and $\frac{4}{4}$ time.

Dotted Quavers and Semiquavers
Staccato (Detached)

Dotted quavers and semiquavers **played staccato (detached)** are separated by a short pause.
Take notice how these notes are written and how they are actually played.

Joy to the World
(Duet)

Handel

Battle Hymn of the Republic
Civil War Song

Steffe

Home work: Write a line of notes using crotchets, dotted crotchets followed by quavers and dotted quavers followed by semiquavers in $\frac{2}{4}$ time.

LESSON 31

OBJECTIVES: 1 To learn the name and fingering of
fourth space E flat.
2. To learn the E flat major scale.
3. Familiar melodies using this key.

Eb Major Scale (Bb, Eb, Ab)

Hymn

Moderato

J. Hatton

Key of ___ flats are ___ .?   This note is ?   This note is ?

Think Count: 1 2 3 4

The Spacious Firmament on High

Maestoso

Haydn

Think Count: 4 1 2 3 4

Silent Night, Holy Night

Andante

Gruber

Key of ___ flats are ___ ?

Think Count: 1 2 & 3 4 5 6

LESSON 32

OBJECTIVES: 1. To learn the name and fingering of
fourth space E natural.
2. Application of acquired knowledge.

Santa Lucia

Neapolitan Boat Song

Rousseau's Hymn

* Da Capo – to beginning

	Points	Your score

(1) In slow $\frac{6}{8}$ time, what does the six mean and what does the eight mean?   7   _____

(2) In slow $\frac{6}{8}$ time, this note [music notation] has _____ counts?   4   _____

(3) In slow $\frac{6}{8}$ time, this note [music notation] has _____ counts?   4   _____

(4) Mark the counts for slow $\frac{6}{8}$ under the following.   5   _____

[music notation]

(5) Divide the following into bars.   5   _____

[music notation]

(6) In fast $\frac{6}{8}$ the count is _____ beats to a bar.   4   _____

(7) In No. 5 above, mark the counts in fast $\frac{6}{8}$ time.   5   _____

(8) These [music notation] are _____?   5   _____

(9) Four (4) of the above notes equal a _____?   4   _____

(10) Divide the following into bars?   5   _____

[music notation]

(11) This 𝄾 is a _____ rest?   4   _____

(12) A [note] is equal to _____ semiquavers.   4   _____

(13) A [note] is equal to _____ semiquavers.   4   _____

(14) Write four (4) bars, using dotted quavers and semiquavers.   5   _____

[music staff]

(15) Divide the following into bars?   5   _____

[music notation]

(16) This note [music notation] is _____ and is played with the _____ valve?   5   _____

(17) This note [music notation] is _____ and is played with the _____ valve?   5   _____

(18) Write the E flat major scale.   5   _____

[music staff]

(19) Sight reading. $\frac{15}{100}$ ══

[music staff]

TEACHER: Write line of notes using dotted quavers and semiquavers, slurs, accidentals, etc.

Printed in Great Britain